The Far Side® GALLERY

2001 DESK CALENDAR
GARY LARSON

The Ink Group

Web Site: www.inkgroup.com

Published and distributed by The Ink Group.
Printed in China on recycled paper.
All dates have been obtained from official sources and were correct at time of printing.

AUSTRALIA
The Ink Group Pty Ltd Publishers
111 Burrows Road, Alexandria
NSW 2015, Australia
Telephone: +61 2 9950 9777
Facsimile: +61 2 9557 8965
email: blackink@inkgroup.com.au

NEW ZEALAND
The Ink Group NZ Ltd
Unit B, 8 Piermark Drive, North Harbour
Albany, Auckland, New Zealand
Telephone: +64 9 415 5529
Facsimile: +64 9 415 5603

**DISTRIBUTED IN THE UNITED
KINGDOM AND EUROPE BY:**
Gibson Greetings International Ltd
Gibson House, Hortonwood 30, Telford
Shropshire TF1 4ET, United Kingdom
Telephone: +44 1952 608333
Facsimile: +44 1952 608363

It's true, of course, that the "C" word has been overused to the point of exhaustion. Need proof? Tune in to your local "classic rock" station and listen for a few minutes. Does *anyone* in the world *really* need to hear Bachman Turner Overdrive's "Takin' Care of Business" again? Ever? Show me the guy out there who's thinking to himself … "Gee, I'm in a 'Desperado' kind of mood …"

We humbly submit that the word "classic" be outlawed from the airwaves and banished from the vocabularies of slick marketing types (present company excluded). Let's make "classic" mean something again! '57 Chevy Bel Air? Yes! The *Mona Lisa*? Of course! The cartoons collected in the "The Far Side® Gallery 2001 Desk Calendar"? ABSOLUTELY!

Collected in this desk calendar, presented in vivid color—one per week—are the most exemplary examples of the cartooning craft as executed by Gary Larson. Think of this calendar as a little Sistine Chapel ceiling that sits on a desk; a pint-sized Beethoven belting out his Fifth Symphony. Or, quite likely the funniest calendar in which you have ever had the pleasure of penciling your dentist appointments and visits to the beauty parlor.

JANUARY

Sunday	Monday	Tuesday	Wednesday	Thursday	Friday	Saturday
31	1 New Year's Day Kwanzaa ends (USA)	2 Day after New Year's Day (New Zealand, Scotland)	3	4	5	6 Epiphany
7	8 Coming of Age Day (Japan)	9	10	11	12	13
14	15 Martin Luther King Day (USA)	16	17	18	19	20 Inauguration Day (USA)
21	22	23	24 Chinese New Year - Year of the Snake	25	26 Australia Day	27
28	29	30	31	1	2	3

December 2000

S	M	T	W	T	F	S
26	27	28	29	30	1	2
3	4	5	6	7	8	9
10	11	12	13	14	15	16
17	18	19	20	21	22	23
24 31	25	26	27	28	29	30

February

S	M	T	W	T	F	S
28	29	30	31	1	2	3
4	5	6	7	8	9	10
11	12	13	14	15	16	17
18	19	20	21	22	23	24
25	26	27	28	1	2	3

NOTES

"Well, let's see—so far, I've got rhythm and I've got music. …
Actually, who could ask for anything more?"

JANUARY

Notes

JANUARY

S	M	T	W	T	F	S
31	1	2	3	4	5	6
7	8	9	10	11	12	13
14	15	16	17	18	19	20
21	22	23	24	25	26	27
28	29	30	31	1	2	3

Monday
1
New Year's Day
Kwanzaa ends (USA)

Tuesday
2
Day after New Year's Day
(New Zealand, Scotland)

Wednesday
3

Thursday
4

Friday
5

Saturday
6
Epiphany

Sunday
7

In the Chicken Museum

JANUARY

Monday

8

Coming of Age Day (Japan)

Tuesday

9

7-45p.m TOTAL ECLIPSE OF THE MOON

Wednesday

10

Thursday

11

Friday

12

JANUARY

S	M	T	W	T	F	S
31	1	2	3	4	5	6
7	8	9	10	11	12	13
14	15	16	17	18	19	20
21	22	23	24	25	26	27
28	29	30	31	1	2	3

Saturday

13

Sunday

14

JANUARY

Monday
15
Martin Luther King Day (USA)

Tuesday
16

Wednesday
17

Thursday
18

Friday
19

JANUARY

S	M	T	W	T	F	S
31	1	2	3	4	5	6
7	8	9	10	11	12	13
14	15	16	17	18	19	20
21	22	23	24	25	26	27
28	29	30	31	1	2	3

Saturday
20
Inauguration Day (USA)

Sunday
21

The elephant's nightmare

JANUARY

Monday
22

Tuesday
23

Wednesday
24

Chinese New Year
- Year of the Snake

Thursday
25

Friday
26

Australia Day

Saturday
27

Sunday
28

JANUARY

S	M	T	W	T	F	S
31	1	2	3	4	5	6
7	8	9	10	11	12	13
14	15	16	17	18	19	20
21	22	23	24	25	26	27
28	29	30	31	1	2	3

FEBRUARY

Sunday	Monday	Tuesday	Wednesday	Thursday	Friday	Saturday
28	29	30	31	1	2 Groundhog Day	3
4	5	6 Waitangi Day (New Zealand)	7	8	9	10
11	12 National Foundation Day (Japan)	13	14 St Valentine's Day	15	16	17
18	19 Presidents' Day (USA)	20	21	22 Washington's Birthday (USA)	23	24
25	26	27	28 Ash Wednesday	1	2	3

January

S	M	T	W	T	F	S
31	1	2	3	4	5	6
7	8	9	10	11	12	13
14	15	16	17	18	19	20
21	22	23	24	25	26	27
28	29	30	31	1	2	3

March

S	M	T	W	T	F	S
25	26	27	28	1	2	3
4	5	6	7	8	9	10
11	12	13	14	15	16	17
18	19	20	21	22	23	24
25	26	27	28	29	30	31

NOTES

"It's this new boyfriend, dear. ... I'm just afraid one day
your father's going to up and blow him away."

JANUARY-FEBRUARY

Monday

29

Tuesday

30

Wednesday

31

Thursday

1

Friday

2

Groundhog Day

Saturday

3

Sunday

4

FEBRUARY

S	M	T	W	T	F	S
28	29	30	31	1	2	3
4	5	6	7	8	9	10
11	12	13	14	15	16	17
18	19	20	21	22	23	24
25	26	27	28	1	2	3

"Ooo! *This* is always amusing. … Here comes Bessie inside her plastic cow ball."

FEBRUARY

Monday

5

Tuesday

6

Waitangi Day (New Zealand)

Wednesday

7

Thursday

8

Friday

9

FEBRUARY

S	M	T	W	T	F	S
28	29	30	31	1	2	3
4	5	6	7	8	9	10
11	12	13	14	15	16	17
18	19	20	21	22	23	24
25	26	27	28	1	2	3

Saturday

10

Sunday

11

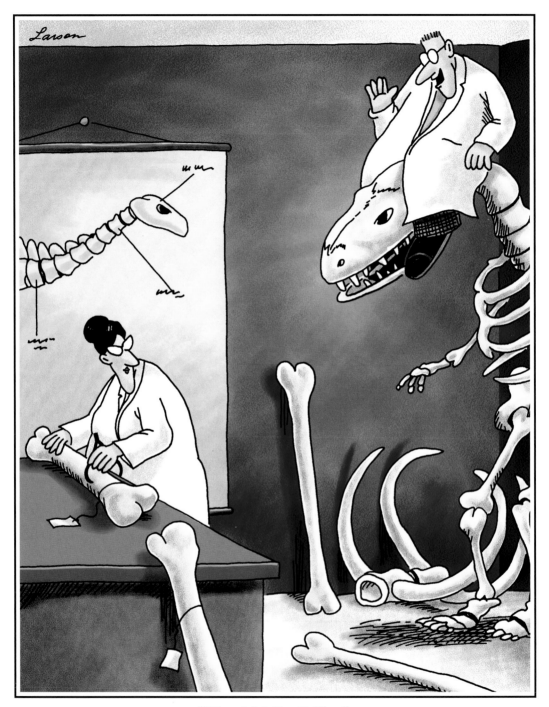

"Hi ... hi, Miss Collins."

FEBRUARY

Monday

12

National Foundation Day (Japan)

Tuesday

13

Wednesday

14

St Valentine's Day

Thursday

15

Friday

16

FEBRUARY

S	M	T	W	T	F	S
28	29	30	31	1	2	3
4	5	6	7	8	9	10
11	12	13	14	15	16	17
18	19	20	21	22	23	24
25	26	27	28	1	2	3

Saturday

17

Sunday

18

Simultaneously all three went for the ball, and the
coconut-like sound of their heads hitting secretly delighted the bird.

FEBRUARY

Notes

Monday

19

Presidents' Day (USA)

Tuesday

20

Wednesday

21

Thursday

22

Washington's Birthday (USA)

Friday

23

Saturday

24

Sunday

25

FEBRUARY

S	M	T	W	T	F	S
28	29	30	31	1	2	3
4	5	6	7	8	9	10
11	12	13	14	15	16	17
18	19	20	21	22	23	24
25	26	27	28	1	2	3

MARCH

Sunday	Monday	Tuesday	Wednesday	Thursday	Friday	Saturday
25	26	27	28	1 First Day of Autumn (Southern Hemisphere) St David's Day	2	3
4 First Sunday of Lent	5 Labour Day (Australia - WA)	6 Eid ul Adha	7	8 International Women's Day	9 Purim	10
11	12 Labour Day (Australia - VIC) Eight Hours Day (Australia - TAS)	13	14	15	16	17 St Patrick's Day
18	19 Canberra Day (Australia - ACT) St Patrick's Day Holiday (Eire. Northern Ireland)	20 Vernal Equinox (Northern Hemisphere)	21	22	23	24
25 Daylight Saving ends (Aust) Summer Time begins (UK. Europe) Mothering Sunday (UK)	26	27 Islamic New Year	28	29	30	31

February

S	M	T	W	T	F	S
28	29	30	31	1	2	3
4	5	6	7	8	9	10
11	12	13	14	15	16	17
18	19	20	21	22	23	24
25	26	27	28	1	2	3

April

S	M	T	W	T	F	S
1	2	3	4	5	6	7
8	9	10	11	12	13	14
15	16	17	18	19	20	21
22	23	24	25	26	27	28
29	30	1	2	3	4	5

NOTES

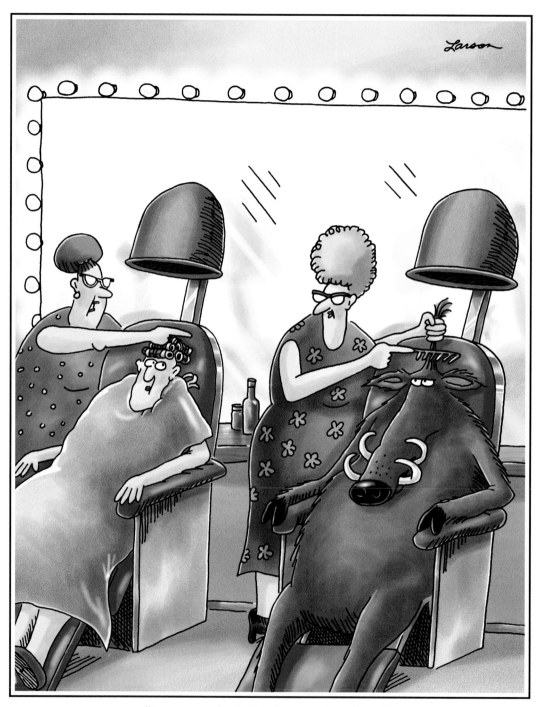

"Betty, you fool! Don't tease that thing!"

FEBRUARY·MARCH

Monday

26

Tuesday

27

Wednesday

28

Ash Wednesday

Thursday

1

First Day of Autumn
(Southern Hemisphere)
St David's Day

Friday

2

Saturday

3

Sunday

4

First Sunday of Lent

MARCH

S	M	T	W	T	F	S
25	26	27	28	1	2	3
4	5	6	7	8	9	10
11	12	13	14	15	16	17
18	19	20	21	22	23	24
25	26	27	28	29	30	31

Fortunately for Sparky, Zeke knew the famous "Rex maneuver."

MARCH

Monday

5

Labour Day (Australia - WA)

Tuesday

6

Eid ul Adha

Wednesday

7

Thursday

8

International Women's Day

Friday

9

Purim

MARCH

S	M	T	W	T	F	S
25	26	27	28	1	2	3
4	5	6	7	8	9	10
11	12	13	14	15	16	17
18	19	20	21	22	23	24
25	26	27	28	29	30	31

Saturday

10

Sunday

11

"My God! It *is* Professor Dickle! … Weinberg, see if you can make out what the devil he was working on, and the rest of you get back to your stations."

MARCH

Notes

Monday
12
Labour Day
(Australia - VIC)

Eight Hours Day
(Australia - TAS)

Tuesday
13

Wednesday
14

Thursday
15

Friday
16

MARCH

S	M	T	W	T	F	S
				1	2	3
4	5	6	7	8	9	10
11	12	13	14	15	16	17
18	19	20	21	22	23	24
25	26	27	28	29	30	31

Saturday
17

St Patrick's Day

Sunday
18

MARCH

_____

_____

_____

_____

_____

_____

_____

_____

_____

_____

_____

_____

_____

_____

_____

Monday
19

Canberra Day
(Australia - ACT)
St Patrick's Day Holiday
(Eire. Northern Ireland)

Tuesday
20

Vernal Equinox
(Northern Hemisphere)

Wednesday
21

Thursday
22

Friday
23

Saturday
24

Sunday
25

Daylight Saving ends
(Australia - NSW, ACT, VIC, TAS, SA)
Summer Time begins (UK, Europe)
Mothering Sunday (UK)

MARCH

S	M	T	W	T	F	S
25	26	27	28	1	2	3
4	5	6	7	8	9	10
11	12	13	14	15	16	17
18	19	20	21	22	23	24
25	26	27	28	29	30	31

APRIL

Sunday	Monday	Tuesday	Wednesday	Thursday	Friday	Saturday
1 April Fool's Day	2	3	4	5	6	7
8 Palm Sunday First Day of Passover	9	10	11	12	13 Good Friday (Western, Orthodox)	14 Easter Saturday (Australia - except VIC, WA)
15 Easter Sunday (Western, Orthodox) Last Day of Passover	16 Easter Monday (Australia, New Zealand, UK - except Scotland)	17	18	19	20	21
22 Earth Day	23 St George's Day	24	25 Anzac Day (Australia, New Zealand) Liberation Day (Italy) Secretaries Day	26	27 Freedom Day (South Africa)	28
29	30 Greenery Day (Japan)					

March

S	M	T	W	T	F	S
			1	2	3	
4	5	6	7	8	9	10
11	12	13	14	15	16	17
18	19	20	21	22	23	24
25	26	27	28	29	30	31

May

S	M	T	W	T	F	S
		1	2	3	4	5
6	7	8	9	10	11	12
13	14	15	16	17	18	19
20	21	22	23	24	25	26
27	28	29	30	31		

NOTES

"Bob! Wake up! Bob! A ship! I think I see a ship! … Where are your glasses?"

MARCH-APRIL

Monday
26

Tuesday
27
Islamic New Year

Wednesday
28

Thursday
29

Friday
30

		APRIL				
S	M	T	W	T	F	S
1	2	3	4	5	6	7
8	9	10	11	12	13	14
15	16	17	18	19	20	21
22	23	24	25	26	27	28
29	30	1	2	3	4	5

Saturday
31

Sunday
1
April Fool's Day

More trouble brewing

APRIL

Monday

2

Tuesday

3

Wednesday

4

Thursday

5

Friday

6

Saturday

7

Sunday

8

Palm Sunday
First Day of Passover

APRIL

S	M	T	W	T	F	S
1	2	3	4	5	6	7
8	9	10	11	12	13	14
15	16	17	18	19	20	21
22	23	24	25	26	27	28
29	30					

"I just *can't* go in there, Bart! ... Some fellow
in there and I are wearing the same kind of hat!"

APRIL

Monday
9

Tuesday
10

Wednesday
11

Thursday
12

Friday
13
Good Friday
(Western, Orthodox)

Saturday
14
Easter Saturday (Australia
- except VIC, WA)

Sunday
15
Easter Sunday
(Western, Orthodox)
Last Day of Passover

APRIL

S	M	T	W	T	F	S
1	2	3	4	5	6	7
8	9	10	11	12	13	14
15	16	17	18	19	20	21
22	23	24	25	26	27	28
29	30	1	2	3	4	5

"It's Vince, all right. It's his nose, his mouth, his fur ...
but his eyes—there's something not quite right about his eyes."

APRIL

Monday
16

Easter Monday
(Australia, New Zealand,
UK - except Scotland)

Tuesday
17

Wednesday
18

Thursday
19

Friday
20

APRIL

S	M	T	W	T	F	S
1	2	3	4	5	6	7
8	9	10	11	12	13	14
15	16	17	18	19	20	21
22	23	24	25	26	27	28
29	30					

Saturday
21

Sunday
22

Earth Day

To his horror, Irving suddenly realized he had failed to
check his own boots before putting them on just minutes ago.

APRIL

_____
_____
_____
_____
_____
_____
_____
_____
_____
_____

APRIL

S	M	T	W	T	F	S
1	2	3	4	5	6	7
8	9	10	11	12	13	14
15	16	17	18	19	20	21
22	23	24	25	26	27	28
29	30	1	2	3	4	5

Monday
23
St George's Day

Tuesday
24

Wednesday
25
Anzac Day (Australia, New Zealand)
Liberation Day (Italy)
Secretaries Day

Thursday
26

Friday
27
Freedom Day (South Africa)

Saturday
28

Sunday
29

MAY

Sunday	Monday	Tuesday	Wednesday	Thursday	Friday	Saturday
29	30	1 Workers Day (South Africa) Labour Day (France, Italy, China)	2	3 Constitution Memorial Day (Japan)	4 People's Holiday (Japan)	5 Children's Day (Japan) Cinco De Mayo (Mexico)
6	7 Labour Day (Aust. - QLD) May Day (Aust. - NT) Early May Bank Holiday (UK, Eire)	8 Victory Day (France)	9	10	11	12
13 Mother's Day (Australia, New Zealand, Canada, USA)	14	15	16	17	18	19 Armed Forces Day (USA)
20	21 Victoria Day (Canada)	22	23	24 Ascension Day	25	26
27	28 Spring Bank Holiday (UK) Shavuot begins Memorial Day observed (USA)	29 Shavuot ends	30	31		

April

S	M	T	W	T	F	S
1	2	3	4	5	6	7
8	9	10	11	12	13	14
15	16	17	18	19	20	21
22	23	24	25	26	27	28
29	30					

June

S	M	T	W	T	F	S
					1	2
3	4	5	6	7	8	9
10	11	12	13	14	15	16
17	18	19	20	21	22	23
24	25	26	27	28	29	30

NOTES

"Hey! Look at me, everybody! I'm a cowboy! … Howdy, howdy, howdy!"

Notes

Monday

30

Greenery Day (Japan)

Tuesday

1

Workers Day (South Africa)
Labour Day (France, Italy, China)
May Day (Germany, Finland)

Wednesday

2

Thursday

3

Constitution Memorial Day (Japan)

Friday

4

People's Holiday (Japan)

Saturday

5

Children's Day (Japan)
Cinco De Mayo (Mexico)

Sunday

6

MAY

S	M	T	W	T	F	S
29	30	1	2	3	4	5
6	7	8	9	10	11	12
13	14	15	16	17	18	19
20	21	22	23	24	25	26
27	28	29	30	31	1	2

"Get, you rascal! Get! … Heaven knows how he
keeps getting in here, Betty, but you better count 'em."

MAY

Monday

7

Labour Day (Australia - QLD)
May Day (Australia - NT)
Early May Bank Holiday (UK, Eire)

Tuesday

8

Victory Day (France)

Wednesday

9

Thursday

10

Friday

11

Saturday

12

Sunday

13

Mother's Day
(Australia, New Zealand,
Canada, USA)

MAY

S	M	T	W	T	F	S
29	30	1	2	3	4	5
6	7	8	9	10	11	12
13	14	15	16	17	18	19
20	21	22	23	24	25	26
27	28	29	30	31	1	2

"OK, crybaby! You want the last soda? Well, let me GET IT READY FOR YOU!"

MAY

Monday

14

Tuesday

15

Wednesday

16

Thursday

17

Friday

18

MAY

S	M	T	W	T	F	S
29	30	1	2	3	4	5
6	7	8	9	10	11	12
13	14	15	16	17	18	19
20	21	22	23	24	25	26
27	28	29	30	31	1	2

Saturday

19

Armed Forces Day (USA)

Sunday

20

"OK, Frank, that's enough. I'm sure the Jeffersons
are quite amazed at your car headlight device."

MAY

Monday

21

Victoria Day (Canada)

Tuesday

22

Wednesday

23

Thursday

24

Ascension Day

Friday

25

Saturday

26

Sunday

27

MAY

S	M	T	W	T	F	S
29	30	1	2	3	4	5
6	7	8	9	10	11	12
13	14	15	16	17	18	19
20	21	22	23	24	25	26
27	28	29	30	31	1	2

J U N E

Sunday	Monday	Tuesday	Wednesday	Thursday	Friday	Saturday
27	28	29	30	31	1 First Day of Winter (Southern Hemisphere)	2
3 Whitsunday	4 Queen's Birthday (New Zealand) Bank Holiday (Eire)	5 World Environment Day	6	7	8	9
10 Trinity Sunday	11 Queen's Birthday (Australia - except WA)	12 Independence Day (The Philippines)	13	14 Corpus Christi Flag Day (USA)	15	16
17 Father's Day (USA, Canada, UK)	18	19	20	21 Summer Solstice (Northern Hemisphere)	22	23
24	25	26	27	28	29	30

May

S	M	T	W	T	F	S
29	30	1	2	3	4	5
6	7	8	9	10	11	12
13	14	15	16	17	18	19
20	21	22	23	24	25	26
27	28	29	30	31	1	2

July

S	M	T	W	T	F	S
1	2	3	4	5	6	7
8	9	10	11	12	13	14
15	16	17	18	19	20	21
22	23	24	25	26	27	28
29	30	31	1	2	3	4

NOTES

MAY-JUNE

Monday

28

Spring Bank Holiday (UK)
Shavuot begins
Memorial Day observed (USA)

Tuesday

29

Shavuot ends

Wednesday

30

Thursday

31

Friday

1

First Day of Winter
(Southern Hemisphere)

Saturday

2

Sunday

3

Whitsunday

JUNE

S	M	T	W	T	F	S
27	28	29	30	31	1	2
3	4	5	6	7	8	9
10	11	12	13	14	15	16
17	18	19	20	21	22	23
24	25	26	27	28	29	30

God makes the snake.

JUNE

Monday

4

Queen's Birthday (New Zealand)
Foundation Day (Australia – WA)
Bank Holiday (Eire)

Tuesday

5

World Environment Day

Wednesday

6

Thursday

7

Friday

8

JUNE

S	M	T	W	T	F	S
27	28	29	30	31	1	2
3	4	5	6	7	8	9
10	11	12	13	14	15	16
17	18	19	20	21	22	23
24	25	26	27	28	29	30

Saturday

9

Sunday

10

Trinity Sunday

As witnesses later recalled, two small dogs just
waltzed into the place, grabbed the cat, and waltzed out.

JUNE

Monday

11

Queen's Birthday
(Australia - except WA)

Tuesday

12

Independence Day (The Philippines)

Wednesday

13

Thursday

14

Corpus Christi
Flag Day (USA)

Friday

15

JUNE

S	M	T	W	T	F	S
27	28	29	30	31	1	2
3	4	5	6	7	8	9
10	11	12	13	14	15	16
17	18	19	20	21	22	23
24	25	26	27	28	29	30

Saturday

16

Sunday

17

Father's Day
(USA, Canada, UK)

"Bear! Bear!"

JUNE

Monday

18

Tuesday

19

Wednesday

20

Thursday

21

Summer Solstice
(Northern Hemisphere)

Friday

22

Saturday

23

Sunday

24

JUNE

S	M	T	W	T	F	S
27	28	29	30	31	1	2
3	4	5	6	7	8	9
10	11	12	13	14	15	16
17	18	19	20	21	22	23
24	25	26	27	28	29	30

J U L Y

Sunday	Monday	Tuesday	Wednesday	Thursday	Friday	Saturday
1 Canada Day / HKSAR Establishment Day (Hong Kong)	2	3	4 Independence Day (USA)	5	6	7
8	9	10	11	12 Battle of the Boyne (Northern Ireland)	13	14 Bastille Day (France)
15	16	17	18	19	20 Marine Day (Japan)	21
22	23	24	25	26	27	28
29	30	31	1	2	3	4

June

S	M	T	W	T	F	S
27	28	29	30	31	1	2
3	4	5	6	7	8	9
10	11	12	13	14	15	16
17	18	19	20	21	22	23
24	25	26	27	28	29	30

August

S	M	T	W	T	F	S
29	30	31	1	2	3	4
5	6	7	8	9	10	11
12	13	14	15	16	17	18
19	20	21	22	23	24	25
26	27	28	29	30	31	1

NOTES

How birds see the world

JUNE - JULY

Notes

Monday
25

Tuesday
26

Wednesday
27

Thursday
28

Friday
29

JULY

S	M	T	W	T	F	S
1	2	3	4	5	6	7
8	9	10	11	12	13	14
15	16	17	18	19	20	21
22	23	24	25	26	27	28
29	30	31	1	2	3	4

Saturday
30

Sunday
1

Canada Day

HKSAR Establishment Day (Hong Kong)

"You're sick, Jessy! … Sick, sick, sick!"

JULY

Monday

2

Tuesday

3

Wednesday

4

Independence Day (USA)

Thursday

5

Friday

6

		JULY			
S	M	T	W	T	F	S
1	2	3	4	5	6	7
8	9	10	11	12	13	14
15	16	17	18	19	20	21
22	23	24	25	26	27	28
29	30	31	1	2	3	4

Saturday

7

Sunday

8

"Say … now *I'm* starting to feel kinda warm!"

JULY

Monday

9

Tuesday

10

Wednesday

11

Thursday

12

Battle of the Boyne
(Northern Ireland)

Friday

13

JULY

S	M	T	W	T	F	S
1	2	3	4	5	6	7
8	9	10	11	12	13	14
15	16	17	18	19	20	21
22	23	24	25	26	27	28
29	30	31	1	2	3	4

Saturday

14

Bastille Day (France)

Sunday

15

JULY

Notes

Monday
16

Tuesday
17

Wednesday
18

Thursday
19

Friday
20

Marine Day (Japan)

Saturday
21

Sunday
22

JULY

S	M	T	W	T	F	S
1	2	3	4	5	6	7
8	9	10	11	12	13	14
15	16	17	18	19	20	21
22	23	24	25	26	27	28
29	30	31	1	2	3	4

"It's time we face reality, my friends. ... We're not exactly rocket scientists."

JULY

Monday
23

Tuesday
24

Wednesday
25

Thursday
26

Friday
27

JULY

S	M	T	W	T	F	S
1	2	3	4	5	6	7
8	9	10	11	12	13	14
15	16	17	18	19	20	21
22	23	24	25	26	27	28
29	30	31	1	2	3	4

Saturday
28

Sunday
29

AUGUST

Sunday	Monday	Tuesday	Wednesday	Thursday	Friday	Saturday
29	30	31	1 Swiss National Day Horses' Birthday	2	3	4
5	6 Picnic Day (Australia - NT) Summer Bank Holiday (Scotland, Eire)	7	8	9	10	11
12	13	14	15 Assumption	16	17	18
19	20	21	22	23	24	25
26	27 Summer Bank Holiday (UK - except Scotland)	28	29	30	31	1

July

S	M	T	W	T	F	S
1	2	3	4	5	6	7
8	9	10	11	12	13	14
15	16	17	18	19	20	21
22	23	24	25	26	27	28
29	30	31	1	2	3	4

September

S	M	T	W	T	F	S
26	27	28	29	30	31	1
2	3	4	5	6	7	8
9	10	11	12	13	14	15
16	17	18	19	20	21	22
23 30	24	25	26	27	28	29

NOTES

"Are you serious? Look at our arms! If anything, I'm *twice* as tan as you are."

JULY-AUGUST

Notes

Monday

30

Tuesday

31

Wednesday

1

Swiss National Day
Horses' Birthday

Thursday

2

Friday

3

Saturday

4

Sunday

5

AUGUST

S	M	T	W	T	F	S
29	30	31	1	2	3	4
5	6	7	8	9	10	11
12	13	14	15	16	17	18
19	20	21	22	23	24	25
26	27	28	29	30	31	1

While Farmer Brown was away, the cows got into the kitchen and
were having the time of their lives—until Betsy's unwitting discovery.

AUGUST

_____
_____
_____
_____
_____
_____
_____
_____
_____
_____
_____
_____
_____
_____
_____

Monday

6

Bank Holiday (Australia – NSW, ACT)
Picnic Day (Australia – NT)
Summer Bank Holiday (Scotland, Eire)

Tuesday

7

Wednesday

8

Thursday

9

Friday

10

Saturday

11

Sunday

12

AUGUST

S	M	T	W	T	F	S
29	30	31	1	2	3	4
5	6	7	8	9	10	11
12	13	14	15	16	17	18
19	20	21	22	23	24	25
26	27	28	29	30	31	1

AUGUST

Monday

13

Tuesday

14

Wednesday

15

Assumption

Thursday

16

Friday

17

Saturday

18

Sunday

19

AUGUST

S	M	T	W	T	F	S
29	30	31	1	2	3	4
5	6	7	8	9	10	11
12	13	14	15	16	17	18
19	20	21	22	23	24	25
26	27	28	29	30	31	1

"Well, so much for the unicorns. …
But, from now on, all carnivores will be confined to 'C' deck."

AUGUST

Monday
20

Tuesday
21

Wednesday
22

Thursday
23

Friday
24

Saturday
25

Sunday
26

AUGUST

S	M	T	W	T	F	S
29	30	31	1	2	3	4
5	6	7	8	9	10	11
12	13	14	15	16	17	18
19	20	21	22	23	24	25
26	27	28	29	30	31	1

SEPTEMBER

Sunday	Monday	Tuesday	Wednesday	Thursday	Friday	Saturday
26	27	28	29	30	31	1 First Day of Spring (Southern Hemisphere)
2 Father's Day (Australia, New Zealand)	3 Labor Day (USA, Canada)	4	5	6	7	8
9	10	11	12	13	14	15 Respect for the Aged Day (Japan)
16 Independence Day (Mexico)	17	18 Rosh Hashanah begins	19 Rosh Hashanah ends	20	21	22 Autumnal Equinox (Northern Hemisphere)
23	24	25	26	27 Yom Kippur	28	29
30						

August

S	M	T	W	T	F	S
29	30	31	1	2	3	4
5	6	7	8	9	10	11
12	13	14	15	16	17	18
19	20	21	22	23	24	25
26	27	28	29	30	31	1

October

S	M	T	W	T	F	S
30	1	2	3	4	5	6
7	8	9	10	11	12	13
14	15	16	17	18	19	20
21	22	23	24	25	26	27
28	29	30	31	1	2	3

NOTES

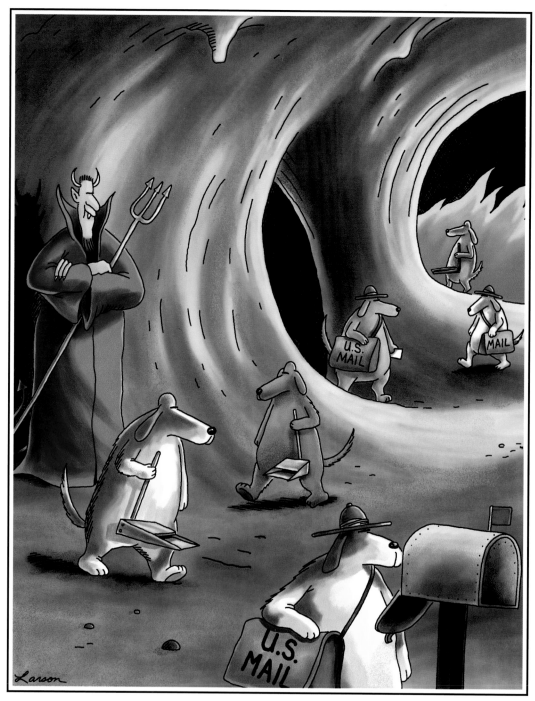

Dog Hell

AUGUST-SEPTEMBER

Notes

Monday

27

Summer Bank Holiday
(UK - except Scotland)

Tuesday

28

Wednesday

29

Thursday

30

Friday

31

SEPTEMBER

S	M	T	W	T	F	S
26	27	28	29	30	31	1
2	3	4	5	6	7	8
9	10	11	12	13	14	15
16	17	18	19	20	21	22
23 / 30	24	25	26	27	28	29

Saturday

1

First Day of Spring
(Southern Hemisphere)

Sunday

2

Father's Day (Australia, New Zealand)

SEPTEMBER

Notes

Monday

3

Labor Day (USA, Canada)

Tuesday

4

Wednesday

5

Thursday

6

Friday

7

SEPTEMBER						
S	M	T	W	T	F	S
26	27	28	29	30	31	1
2	3	4	5	6	7	8
9	10	11	12	13	14	15
16	17	18	19	20	21	22
23 30	24	25	26	27	28	29

Saturday

8

Sunday

9

It was very late, and Raymond, fighting insomnia,
went for a midnight snack. Unfortunately, he never saw the duck blind.

SEPTEMBER

Monday
10

Tuesday
11

Wednesday
12

Thursday
13

Friday
14

Saturday
15

Respect for the Aged Day (Japan)

Sunday
16

Independence Day (Mexico)

SEPTEMBER

S	M	T	W	T	F	S
26	27	28	29	30	31	1
2	3	4	5	6	7	8
9	10	11	12	13	14	15
16	17	18	19	20	21	22
23 / 30	24	25	26	27	28	29

Suddenly, amidst all the confusion, Fifi seized the controls and saved the day.

SEPTEMBER

Monday
17

Tuesday
18
Rosh Hashanah begins

Wednesday
19
Rosh Hashanah ends

Thursday
20

Friday
21

SEPTEMBER

S	M	T	W	T	F	S
26	27	28	29	30	31	1
2	3	4	5	6	7	8
9	10	11	12	13	14	15
16	17	18	19	20	21	22
23 / 30	24	25	26	27	28	29

Saturday
22
Autumnal Equinox
(Northern Hemisphere)

Sunday
23

SEPTEMBER

Monday
24

Tuesday
25

Wednesday
26

Thursday
27

Yom Kippur

Friday
28

Saturday
29

Sunday
30

SEPTEMBER

S	M	T	W	T	F	S
26	27	28	29	30	31	1
2	3	4	5	6	7	8
9	10	11	12	13	14	15
16	17	18	19	20	21	22
23 30	24	25	26	27	28	29

OCTOBER

Sunday	Monday	Tuesday	Wednesday	Thursday	Friday	Saturday
30	1 Queen's Birthday (Australia - WA) Labour Day (Australia - ACT. NSW. SA)	2 First Day of Tabernacles	3 Second Day of Tabernacles National Day (Germany)	4	5	6
7 Daylight Saving begins (Australia - TAS)	8 Thanksgiving (Canada) Columbus Day (USA) Sports Day (Japan)	9	10	11	12	13
14	15	16	17	18	19	20
21	22 Labour Day (New Zealand)	23	24 United Nations Day	25	26	27
28 Daylight Saving begins (Australia - except TAS) Summer Time ends (UK. Europe)	29 Bank Holiday (Eire)	30	31 Halloween	1	2	3

September

S	M	T	W	T	F	S
26	27	28	29	30	31	1
2	3	4	5	6	7	8
9	10	11	12	13	14	15
16	17	18	19	20	21	22
23 30	24	25	26	27	28	29

November

S	M	T	W	T	F	S
28	29	30	31	1	2	3
4	5	6	7	8	9	10
11	12	13	14	15	16	17
18	19	20	21	22	23	24
25	26	27	28	29	30	1

NOTES

Donning his new canine decoder, Professor Schwartzman becomes
the first human being on Earth to hear what barking dogs are saying.

OCTOBER

Monday

1

National Day (China)
Queen's Birthday (Australia - WA)
Labour Day (Australia - ACT, NSW, SA)

Tuesday

2

First Day of Tabernacles

Wednesday

3

Second Day of Tabernacles
National Day (Germany)

Thursday

4

Friday

5

OCTOBER

S	M	T	W	T	F	S
30	1	2	3	4	5	6
7	8	9	10	11	12	13
14	15	16	17	18	19	20
21	22	23	24	25	26	27
28	29	30	31	1	2	3

Saturday

6

Sunday

7

Daylight Saving begins
(Australia - TAS)

OCTOBER

Monday

8

Thanksgiving (Canada)
Columbus Day (USA)
Sports Day (Japan)

Tuesday

9

Wednesday

10

Thursday

11

Friday

12

OCTOBER

S	M	T	W	T	F	S
30	1	2	3	4	5	6
7	8	9	10	11	12	13
14	15	16	17	18	19	20
21	22	23	24	25	26	27
28	29	30	31	1	2	3

Saturday

13

Sunday

14

"Come with us, ma'am—and if I were you, I'd get a good lawyer.
No one's gonna buy that my-husband-was-only-hibernating story."

OCTOBER

Monday

15

Tuesday

16

Wednesday

17

Thursday

18

Friday

19

OCTOBER

S	M	T	W	T	F	S
30	1	2	3	4	5	6
7	8	9	10	11	12	13
14	15	16	17	18	19	20
21	22	23	24	25	26	27
28	29	30	31	1	2	3

Saturday

20

Sunday

21

"Just stay in the cab, Vern … maybe that bear's hurt and maybe he ain't."

OCTOBER

Monday

22

Labour Day (New Zealand)

Tuesday

23

Wednesday

24

United Nations Day

Thursday

25

Friday

26

Saturday

27

Sunday

28

Daylight Saving begins
(Australia - NSW, ACT, VIC, SA)
Summer Time ends (UK, Europe)

OCTOBER

S	M	T	W	T	F	S
30	1	2	3	4	5	6
7	8	9	10	11	12	13
14	15	16	17	18	19	20
21	22	23	24	25	26	27
28	29	30	31	1	2	3

NOVEMBER

Sunday	Monday	Tuesday	Wednesday	Thursday	Friday	Saturday
28	29	30	31	1 All Saints Day	2 All Souls Day	3 Culture Day (Japan) All Saints Day (Finland)
4	5	6 Melbourne Cup Day (Australia - Melbourne only)	7	8	9	10
11 Armistice Day Remembrance Day (Canada) Veterans' Day (USA)	12 Veterans' Day observed (USA)	13	14	15	16	17 Ramadan begins
18	19	20	21	22 Thanksgiving (USA)	23 Labor Thanksgiving Day (Japan)	24
25	26	27	28	29	30 St Andrew's Day	1

October

S	M	T	W	T	F	S
30	1	2	3	4	5	6
7	8	9	10	11	12	13
14	15	16	17	18	19	20
21	22	23	24	25	26	27
28	29	30	31	1	2	3

December

S	M	T	W	T	F	S
25	26	27	28	29	30	1
2	3	4	5	6	7	8
9	10	11	12	13	14	15
16	17	18	19	20	21	22
23	24	25	26	27	28	29
30	31					

NOTES

"It's a fax from your dog, Mr. Dansworth. It looks like your cat."

OCTOBER-NOVEMBER

Monday
29
Bank Holiday (Eire)

Tuesday
30

Wednesday
31
Halloween

Thursday
1
All Saints Day

Friday
2
All Souls Day

NOVEMBER						
S	M	T	W	T	F	S
28	29	30	31	1	2	3
4	5	6	7	8	9	10
11	12	13	14	15	16	17
18	19	20	21	22	23	24
25	26	27	28	29	30	1

Saturday
3
Culture Day (Japan)
All Saints Day (Finland)

Sunday
4

Hank knew this place well. He need only wait. …
The deer would come, the deer would come.

NOVEMBER

Monday

5

Tuesday

6

Melbourne Cup Day
(Australia - Melbourne only)

Wednesday

7

Thursday

8

Friday

9

Saturday

10

Sunday

11

Armistice Day
Remembrance Day (Canada)
Veterans' Day (USA)

NOVEMBER

S	M	T	W	T	F	S
28	29	30	31	1	2	3
4	5	6	7	8	9	10
11	12	13	14	15	16	17
18	19	20	21	22	23	24
25	26	27	28	29	30	1

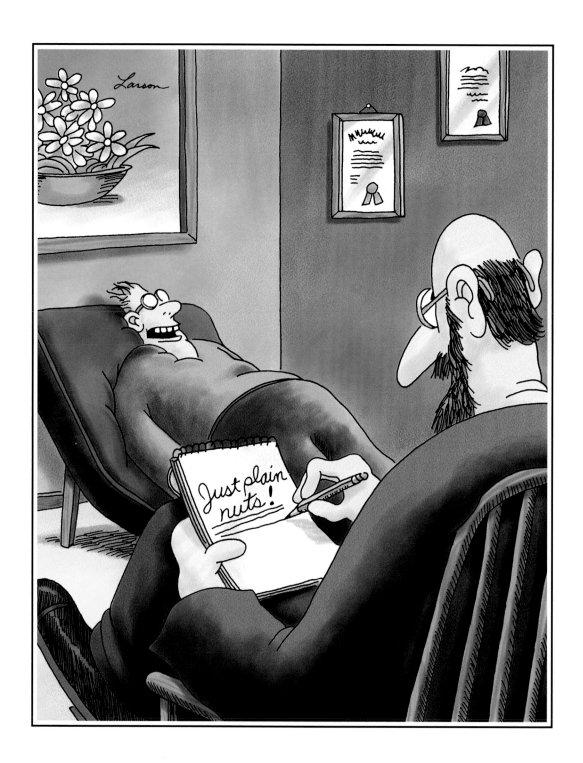

NOVEMBER

Notes

Monday

12

Veterans' Day observed (USA)

Tuesday

13

Wednesday

14

Thursday

15

Friday

16

Saturday

17

Ramadan begins

Sunday

18

NOVEMBER

S	M	T	W	T	F	S
28	29	30	31	1	2	3
4	5	6	7	8	9	10
11	12	13	14	15	16	17
18	19	20	21	22	23	24
25	26	27	28	29	30	1

Hell's Cafeteria

NOVEMBER

Notes

Monday
19

Tuesday
20

Wednesday
21

Thursday
22

Thanksgiving (USA)

Friday
23

Labor Thanksgiving Day (Japan)

Saturday
24

Sunday
25

NOVEMBER

S	M	T	W	T	F	S
28	29	30	31	1	2	3
4	5	6	7	8	9	10
11	12	13	14	15	16	17
18	19	20	21	22	23	24
25	26	27	28	29	30	1

DECEMBER

Sunday	Monday	Tuesday	Wednesday	Thursday	Friday	Saturday
25	26	27	28	29	30	1 First Day of Summer (Southern Hemisphere)
2 First Sunday in Advent	3	4	5	6 Independence Day (Finland)	7	8
9	10 First Day of Chanukah Human Rights Day	11	12 Fiesta of Our Lady of Guadalupe (Mexico)	13	14	15
16	17 Last Day of Chanukah	18	19	20	21 Winter Solstice (Northern Hemisphere)	22
23	24 Christmas Eve	25	26 Boxing Day Proclamation Day (Australia - SA)	27	28	29
30	31 New Year's Eve	Christmas Day	Kwanzaa begins (USA)			

November

S	M	T	W	T	F	S
28	29	30	31	1	2	3
4	5	6	7	8	9	10
11	12	13	14	15	16	17
18	19	20	21	22	23	24
25	26	27	28	29	30	1

January 2002

S	M	T	W	T	F	S
30	31	1	2	3	4	5
6	7	8	9	10	11	12
13	14	15	16	17	18	19
20	21	22	23	24	25	26
27	28	29	30	31	1	2

NOTES

"Well, yes, there is a downside, Fluffy. … When we kill her, the pampering will end."

NOVEMBER - DECEMBER

Monday

26

Tuesday

27

Wednesday

28

Thursday

29

Friday

30

St Andrew's Day

		DECEMBER				
S	M	T	W	T	F	S
25	26	27	28	29	30	1
2	3	4	5	6	7	8
9	10	11	12	13	14	15
16	17	18	19	20	21	22
23 30	24 31	25	26	27	28	29

Saturday

1

First Day of Summer
(Southern Hemisphere)

Sunday

2

First Sunday in Advent

DECEMBER

Monday

3

Tuesday

4

Wednesday

5

Thursday

6

Independence Day (Finland)

Friday

7

Saturday

8

Sunday

9

DECEMBER

S	M	T	W	T	F	S
25	26	27	28	29	30	1
2	3	4	5	6	7	8
9	10	11	12	13	14	15
16	17	18	19	20	21	22
23 30	24 31	25	26	27	28	29

"The fool! … He's on the keyboard!"

DECEMBER

Notes

Monday

10

First Day of Chanukah
Human Rights Day

Tuesday

11

Wednesday

12

Fiesta of Our Lady of
Guadalupe (Mexico)

Thursday

13

Friday

14

Saturday

15

Sunday

16

DECEMBER

S	M	T	W	T	F	S
25	26	27	28	29	30	1
2	3	4	5	6	7	8
9	10	11	12	13	14	15
16	17	18	19	20	21	22
23	24	25	26	27	28	29
30	31					

"The picture's pretty bleak, gentlemen. ... The world's climates are changing, the mammals are taking over, and we all have a brain about the size of a walnut."

DECEMBER

Monday
17
Last Day of Chanukah

Tuesday
18

Wednesday
19

Thursday
20

Friday
21
Winter Solstice
(Northern Hemisphere)

Saturday
22

Sunday
23

DECEMBER

S	M	T	W	T	F	S
25	26	27	28	29	30	1
2	3	4	5	6	7	8
9	10	11	12	13	14	15
16	17	18	19	20	21	22
23 30	24 31	25	26	27	28	29

"Well, look who's excited to see you back from being de-clawed."

DECEMBER

Monday
24
Christmas Eve
Emperor's Birthday (Japan)

Tuesday
25
Christmas Day

Wednesday
26
Boxing Day
(Australia, New Zealand, UK, Canada)
Proclamation Day (Australia - SA)
Kwanzaa begins (USA)

Thursday
27

Friday
28

Saturday
29

Sunday
30

DECEMBER

S	M	T	W	T	F	S
25	26	27	28	29	30	1
2	3	4	5	6	7	8
9	10	11	12	13	14	15
16	17	18	19	20	21	22
23 30	24 31	25	26	27	28	29

"Well, they finally came … but before I go, let's see you roll over a couple times."

Notes

Monday

31

New Year's Eve

Tuesday

1

Wednesday

2

Thursday

3

Friday

4

JANUARY

S	M	T	W	T	F	S
30	31	1	2	3	4	5
6	7	8	9	10	11	12
13	14	15	16	17	18	19
20	21	22	23	24	25	26
27	28	29	30	31	1	2

Saturday

5

Sunday

6

January 2002

February

March

April

May

June

July 2002

August

September

October

November

December

January 2000

S	M	T	W	T	F	S
26	27	28	29	30	31	1
2	3	4	5	6	7	8
9	10	11	12	13	14	15
16	17	18	19	20	21	22
23 / 30	24 / 31	25	26	27	28	29

February 2000

S	M	T	W	T	F	S
30	31	1	2	3	4	5
6	7	8	9	10	11	12
13	14	15	16	17	18	19
20	21	22	23	24	25	26
27	28	29	1	2	3	4

March 2000

S	M	T	W	T	F	S
27	28	29	1	2	3	4
5	6	7	8	9	10	11
12	13	14	15	16	17	18
19	20	21	22	23	24	25
26	27	28	29	30	31	1

April 2000

S	M	T	W	T	F	S
26	27	28	29	30	31	1
2	3	4	5	6	7	8
9	10	11	12	13	14	15
16	17	18	19	20	21	22
23 / 30	24	25	26	27	28	29

May 2000

S	M	T	W	T	F	S
30	1	2	3	4	5	6
7	8	9	10	11	12	13
14	15	16	17	18	19	20
21	22	23	24	25	26	27
28	29	30	31	1	2	3

June 2000

S	M	T	W	T	F	S
28	29	30	31	1	2	3
4	5	6	7	8	9	10
11	12	13	14	15	16	17
18	19	20	21	22	23	24
25	26	27	28	29	30	1

July 2000

S	M	T	W	T	F	S
25	26	27	28	29	30	1
2	3	4	5	6	7	8
9	10	11	12	13	14	15
16	17	18	19	20	21	22
23 / 30	24 / 31	25	26	27	28	29

August 2000

S	M	T	W	T	F	S
30	31	1	2	3	4	5
6	7	8	9	10	11	12
13	14	15	16	17	18	19
20	21	22	23	24	25	26
27	28	29	30	31	1	2

September 2000

S	M	T	W	T	F	S
27	28	29	30	31	1	2
3	4	5	6	7	8	9
10	11	12	13	14	15	16
17	18	19	20	21	22	23
24	25	26	27	28	29	30

October 2000

S	M	T	W	T	F	S
1	2	3	4	5	6	7
8	9	10	11	12	13	14
15	16	17	18	19	20	21
22	23	24	25	26	27	28
29	30	31	1	2	3	4

November 2000

S	M	T	W	T	F	S
29	30	31	1	2	3	4
5	6	7	8	9	10	11
12	13	14	15	16	17	18
19	20	21	22	23	24	25
26	27	28	29	30	1	2

December 2000

S	M	T	W	T	F	S
26	27	28	29	30	1	2
3	4	5	6	7	8	9
10	11	12	13	14	15	16
17	18	19	20	21	22	23
24 / 31	25	26	27	28	29	30

January 2001

S	M	T	W	T	F	S
31	1	2	3	4	5	6
7	8	9	10	11	12	13
14	15	16	17	18	19	20
21	22	23	24	25	26	27
28	29	30	31	1	2	3

February 2001

S	M	T	W	T	F	S
28	29	30	31	1	2	3
4	5	6	7	8	9	10
11	12	13	14	15	16	17
18	19	20	21	22	23	24
25	26	27	28	1	2	3

March 2001

S	M	T	W	T	F	S
25	26	27	28	1	2	3
4	5	6	7	8	9	10
11	12	13	14	15	16	17
18	19	20	21	22	23	24
25	26	27	28	29	30	31

April 2001

S	M	T	W	T	F	S
1	2	3	4	5	6	7
8	9	10	11	12	13	14
15	16	17	18	19	20	21
22	23	24	25	26	27	28
29	30	1	2	3	4	5

May 2001

S	M	T	W	T	F	S
29	30	1	2	3	4	5
6	7	8	9	10	11	12
13	14	15	16	17	18	19
20	21	22	23	24	25	26
27	28	29	30	31	1	2

June 2001

S	M	T	W	T	F	S
27	28	29	30	31	1	2
3	4	5	6	7	8	9
10	11	12	13	14	15	16
17	18	19	20	21	22	23
24	25	26	27	28	29	30

July 2001

S	M	T	W	T	F	S
1	2	3	4	5	6	7
8	9	10	11	12	13	14
15	16	17	18	19	20	21
22	23	24	25	26	27	28
29	30	31	1	2	3	4

August 2001

S	M	T	W	T	F	S
29	30	31	1	2	3	4
5	6	7	8	9	10	11
12	13	14	15	16	17	18
19	20	21	22	23	24	25
26	27	28	29	30	31	1

September 2001

S	M	T	W	T	F	S
26	27	28	29	30	31	1
2	3	4	5	6	7	8
9	10	11	12	13	14	15
16	17	18	19	20	21	22
23 / 30	24	25	26	27	28	29

October 2001

S	M	T	W	T	F	S
30	1	2	3	4	5	6
7	8	9	10	11	12	13
14	15	16	17	18	19	20
21	22	23	24	25	26	27
28	29	30	31	1	2	3

November 2001

S	M	T	W	T	F	S
28	29	30	31	1	2	3
4	5	6	7	8	9	10
11	12	13	14	15	16	17
18	19	20	21	22	23	24
25	26	27	28	29	30	

December 2001

S	M	T	W	T	F	S
25	26	27	28	29	30	1
2	3	4	5	6	7	8
9	10	11	12	13	14	15
16	17	18	19	20	21	22
23 / 30	24 / 31	25	26	27	28	29

January 2002

S	M	T	W	T	F	S
30	31	1	2	3	4	5
6	7	8	9	10	11	12
13	14	15	16	17	18	19
20	21	22	23	24	25	26
27	28	29	30	31	1	2

February 2002

S	M	T	W	T	F	S
27	28	29	30	31	1	2
3	4	5	6	7	8	9
10	11	12	13	14	15	16
17	18	19	20	21	22	23
24	25	26	27	28	1	2

March 2002

S	M	T	W	T	F	S
24	25	26	27	28	1	2
3	4	5	6	7	8	9
10	11	12	13	14	15	16
17	18	19	20	21	22	23
24/31	25	26	27	28	29	30

April 2002

S	M	T	W	T	F	S
31	1	2	3	4	5	6
7	8	9	10	11	12	13
14	15	16	17	18	19	20
21	22	23	24	25	26	27
28	29	30	1	2	3	4

May 2002

S	M	T	W	T	F	S
28	29	30	1	2	3	4
5	6	7	8	9	10	11
12	13	14	15	16	17	18
19	20	21	22	23	24	25
26	27	28	29	30	31	1

June 2002

S	M	T	W	T	F	S
26	27	28	29	30	31	1
2	3	4	5	6	7	8
9	10	11	12	13	14	15
16	17	18	19	20	21	22
23/30	24	25	26	27	28	29

July 2002

S	M	T	W	T	F	S
30	1	2	3	4	5	6
7	8	9	10	11	12	13
14	15	16	17	18	19	20
21	22	23	24	25	26	27
28	29	30	31	1	2	3

August 2002

S	M	T	W	T	F	S
28	29	30	31	1	2	3
4	5	6	7	8	9	10
11	12	13	14	15	16	17
18	19	20	21	22	23	24
25	26	27	28	29	30	31

September 2002

S	M	T	W	T	F	S
1	2	3	4	5	6	7
8	9	10	11	12	13	14
15	16	17	18	19	20	21
22	23	24	25	26	27	28
29	30	1	2	3	4	5

October 2002

S	M	T	W	T	F	S
29	30	1	2	3	4	5
6	7	8	9	10	11	12
13	14	15	16	17	18	19
20	21	22	23	24	25	26
27	28	29	30	31	1	2

November 2002

S	M	T	W	T	F	S
27	28	29	30	31	1	2
3	4	5	6	7	8	9
10	11	12	13	14	15	16
17	18	19	20	21	22	23
24	25	26	27	28	29	30

December 2002

S	M	T	W	T	F	S
1	2	3	4	5	6	7
8	9	10	11	12	13	14
15	16	17	18	19	20	21
22	23	24	25	26	27	28
29	30	31	1	2	3	4

NAMES & NUMBERS

NAMES & NUMBERS

_____ _____
_____ _____
_____ _____
_____ _____
_____ _____
_____ _____
_____ _____
_____ _____
_____ _____
_____ _____
_____ _____
_____ _____
_____ _____
_____ _____
_____ _____
_____ _____